CHARLES DICKENS was born on February 7, 1812, in Landport, Portsea, England. He died in his Gads Hill home in Kent on June 9, 1870. The second of eight children of a family continually plagued by debt, the young Dickens came to know not only hunger and privation—but also the horror of the infamous debtors' prison and the evils of child labor. A turn of fortune in the shape of a legacy brought release from the nightmare of prison and "slave" factories and afforded Dickens the opportunity of two years' formal schooling at Wellington House Academy. He worked as an attorney's clerk and newspaper reporter until his *Sketches by Boz* (1836) and *Pickwick Papers* (1837) brought him the amazing and instant success that was to be his for the remainder of his life. In later years the pressure of serial writing, editorial duties, lectures, and social commitments led to his separation from Catherine Hogarth after twenty-three years of marriage. It also hastened his death at the age of fifty-eight, characteristically while still engaged in a multitude of work.

A Tale

CHARLES DICKENS

of Two Cities

WITH AN AFTERWORD BY
Edgar Johnson

 A SIGNET CLASSIC

Published by
THE NEW AMERICAN LIBRARY, New York and Toronto
THE NEW ENGLISH LIBRARY LIMITED, London

SIGNET TRADEMARK REG. U.S. PAT. OFF. AND FOREIGN COUNTRIES
REGISTERED TRADEMARK—MARCA REGISTRADA
HECHO EN CHICAGO, U.S.A.

SIGNET CLASSICS are published *in the United States*
by The New American Library, Inc., 1301 Avenue of the
Americas, New York, New York 10019, *in Canada* by The
New American Library of Canada Limited, 295 King
Street East, Toronto 2, Ontario, *in the United Kingdom*
by The New English Library Limited, Barnard's Inn,
Holborn, London, E.C. 1, England.

PRINTED IN THE UNITED STATES OF AMERICA